River of Gifts

River of Gifts

by

Sherrill Silberling

artwork by

JoAnne Doyle

This book is in memory of Florence, my mother, whose imagination was as vivid as the blue of her eyes. Tuned to the drama and humor of life, she was a master storyteller who knew how to look closely to find beauty and how to practice the art of fun. On her 100th birthday Florence expressed her desire to live forever. In her stories, she does.

With love and thanks to . . .

my cousins for greeting the concept of this book with excitement.

Pat for assuring me that these stories are worth sharing.

Don, whose never-ending patience with my impatience, shrewd reading and rereading, design sense, and technical expertise have guided this collection to publication.

Donna, whose enthusiasm shifts me from park to drive. Her perseverance, eye for detail, and meticulous editing skills remind me that greater precision is always attainable and that two perfectionists actually can collaborate amiably. We met when we were 7-years-old. I'm so grateful that life just keeps reintroducing us.

Table of Contents

Preface

"Not many people had the childhood I had," my then 92-year-old mother Florence told me one afternoon over a cup of tea at the kitchen table. That was how she summarized growing up in the second and third decades of the twentieth century. What she remembered were the joy of loving parents, who laughed and played with their growing family, and the close companionship of her siblings. She also recalled in detail their "cute" red-roofed, rambling white house surrounded by fruit trees and gardens and pathways to the woods, all encircled by mountains.

Three of the four stories in this book grew from tiny seeds, details lifted from my mother's narratives. They are a blend of fact and fiction. While Florence narrates the last two stories, only *The Gift*, told in the real Florence's own voice, is truth as she remembered it. The setting for all the stories is real—Pennsylvania's Anthracite Region.

Established in 1811, Schuylkill (pronounced skoolkill) County, named after the Schuylkill River which flows to Philadelphia, is located in the east central part of the state. It is a geographically diverse county with farmlands, communities of various sizes, woods, lakes, and, what was for a long time most important, mountains of buried coal. Hard coal. Anthracite. The rich black resource, discovered in 1711 or possibly even earlier, made the region a wealthy industrial center and became a source of income when it was shipped to major cities. By the middle of the twentieth century, however, demand for coal had diminished. Oil and later natural gas gradually replaced coal. Environmentally friendly, sustainable energy sources began to grow in popularity. As the third decade of the twenty-first century begins, wind farms in the northern part of the county stretch along the mountain ridges while solar panels are being installed from one end of the county to the other. In a few locations strip mining still takes place and accumulations of mining waste remain visible although reclamation efforts have erased many vestiges of the process. Coal operations continue, but they are few.

Pottsville, the county seat with its central location and varied neighborhoods including mansions built by financiers, railroad executives, and coal barons, was a busy, prosperous city. Just outside Pottsville in a little borough with its own school, the rambling white house was located. My mother remembered that it seemed always to be filled with light.

These holiday stories are about Alice and Charlie and their five oldest children whom you will meet. Eventually five more children—Harvey, Elsie, Grace, Glenn, and Alan—joined the family. Because of the neighboring coal company's expansion, a year after Glenn's birth the family was forced to leave their idyllic location. Their new house sat on a hilltop within Pottsville's city limits and offered a view of the city, hills of huckleberries to pick, and new mountains to explore. There the birth of the tenth child completed the family. A second group of storytellers, the "little kids," continued the family tradition, and a new era of storytelling began. The stories that follow are a tribute to this family of 12 and to the three L's—family Love, Loyalty, and Laughter—they personify.

2020

The History of Schuylkill County, published in 1950 by the School District of Pottsville, was a source for historical and mining information.

A Complete Dinner

"*D*awever Louey!" Alice exclaimed when she scanned the shelf reserved for canned vegetables and found only one can of corn. No one knew who Louey was, and no one knew what Dawever meant or even how to spell it, but the children in the family knew that when their mother said it, things weren't the way they should be.

On the day before Christmas, with the turkey ready for roasting and warm, golden-crusted pies temporarily resting on the polished black surface of the coal stove, only one can of corn on the pantry shelf foretold an incomplete Christmas Day feast. Now this was before frozen vegetables in magic bags ready for the microwave and before fresh vegetables flown in from faraway fields. This was the era of canned vegetables with their brightly painted pictures on the labels—corn a brighter yellow than any ever harvested. On this particular

Christmas Eve day, only one such can was available to feed a hungry, energetic family.

Rummaging in her little white change purse, Alice withdrew a few coins and summoned Arthur and Florence, the oldest children, for the mission. Planting the coins deep in Arthur's wooly pocket, Alice gave instructions for the trek to Mrs. Wheeler's store, not for the candy in the store's glass case that they always eyed longingly but for a can of corn to make Christmas dinner complete.

Arthur and Florence pulled on their high boots, wriggled into their warmest jackets, unfolded their hats to cover their ears, and plunged their hands into mittens before pushing open the door. Just as they were ready to meet the cold, little Mimi started to wail that she wanted to go too like she always did when anyone went anywhere.

"Not this time," Arthur told her sternly. "You won't be able to walk all that way in the snow, and you've gotten too heavy to ride on my shoulders." Mimi's eyes, behind her round glasses, spilled tears, and her lower lip trembled.

"Maybe we could pull her on her sled," Florence suggested, never able to resist Mimi's pleas.

"A wonderful idea!" Alice agreed. "A sleigh ride is just the thing for this little one overflowing with Santa excitement." Unwilling to allow the youngest member of the family to be disappointed on the day before Christmas and foreseeing that an unhappy little girl would divert her sisters Reenie and Lucy from their pre-holiday chores, Alice felt sure the snowy outing was a perfect solution for everyone. "But," Arthur began, then stopped as his mother, to reinforce her decision, bundled Mimi into her pink snow pants, shiny black boots, and pink-trimmed, hooded white jacket with fuzzy mittens attached to the sleeves.

Grumbling, Arthur tramped across fresh snow, at times slipping a little on the packed, icy layer concealed beneath it, and from the shed removed the sled with a seat built on top for a small child. Mimi climbed in, Florence wrapped her in the thick gray blanket reserved for winter excursions, and the three set off for the store with Arthur pulling the sled and Florence dashing ahead as she always did.

The day was cold, the sky was nearly covered by dark clouds with small patches of pale blue between, and the children's breath made puffy white clouds in the frigid air. Up the steep hill they climbed, then down the other side through evergreens trimmed in white, then over a field of trees wearing only their thin bark for protection against the chill. When the trio reached the rusted iron bridge, they walked more cautiously because the surface was slick and slippery under the light snow that had fallen throughout the previous night. Beneath them the river rushed with heavy, late-autumn rain.

From the far side of the bridge, only a short climb took them into a neighborhood of tall, shingled houses where a narrow alley led to Mrs.

Wheeler's one-room store. The bell on the door jingled merrily as the children entered the tiny emporium with its shelves of canned goods reaching nearly to the ceiling and its wood-framed, glass case of penny candies that enticed young customers with promises of chewy, sweet delights. Hearing the bell, Mrs. Wheeler made her laborious journey from her living area in the back and smiled her pointy-toothed welcome. A large woman wearing her customary flowered apron, she breathed heavily as she asked them what they needed.

"One can of corn," said Arthur, taking charge of the transaction and reaching into his pocket for the money his mother had put there. When he withdrew it, he discovered three extra pennies his mother had included as she sometimes did for a treat for each child. Hand outstretched, he showed his sisters the pennies on his palm, and they quickly turned to the candy case to determine what they would purchase. Arthur, because he liked to defy their name, chose a jawbreaker, which he knew would turn into many colors on his tongue. Florence chose a coconut strip with pretty pastel stripes, Mimi, a Mary Jane in its distinctive yellow and red wrapping. And then Mrs. Wheeler did the unexpected. "Merry Christmas," she said, opening a small paper bag and dropping in a second jawbreaker, coconut strip, and Mary Jane. She handed the sugary surprises to Florence.

After excited thank-you's and payment, the three children emerged into the cold December air. The errand was accomplished, and, except for the pleasant surprise, the trip had been an ordinary one, so far.

Arthur helped Mimi into her seat on the sled, Florence tucked the blanket around her and unwrapped her Mary Jane, and each child popped the purchased candy into his or her expectant mouth before beginning the walk home. Florence nestled the bag with extra candy into her deep pocket to eat later. Back through the narrow alley and the neighborhood of tall, shingled houses and down the short hill Arthur and Florence trudged with Mimi riding behind sucking on her taffy and cradling the can of corn in one arm like a mother with an infant.

Beginning to cross the bridge, Arthur noticed that the surface seemed more slippery. "It's colder now," he told Florence and warned her to be careful. Just as his big-brother warning was delivered, his right foot hit ice. He skidded and struggled to regain his balance, but both feet slid in one direction, his body in another, and, in the instant he fell, the sled rope slipped from his hands. Mimi uttered one high-pitched sound as the can of corn escaped her grasp. Her sled found the space between the horizontal bars on the sides of the bridge, hurtled through the air, and crashed into the dark, turbulent river.

"Mimi!" Florence screamed, trying to scramble between the bars and drop into the water to rescue her little sister, but Arthur hung on to one of her ankles as he struggled to stand. Scrambling to his feet, he grabbed Florence's jacket and pulled her off the bridge and down a slope that led to an overgrown path beside the racing river. Without a word they both began running, trying desperately to keep Mimi's pink-trimmed jacket in sight as her sled rode the current of the frigid river in pursuit of a bobbing can of corn.

Every time they caught sight of her, they yelled, "Hold tight, Mimi," even though they realized that their little sister couldn't possibly hear them. One mile, two miles—the chase seemed endless until gradually the river narrowed and rocks and trees jutted from its banks. Arthur and Florence thought they saw Mimi's sled stop, and then they lost sight of her completely.

With terror tearing at their throats, they ran faster and faster until ahead they saw the runaway sled on the riverbank and Mimi being carried toward houses not far from the water. By the time Arthur and Florence arrived at the rescue spot, Mimi, clutching the can of corn that had been plucked from the water by one of her rescuers, was being soothed by a woman who had carried her to her porch step where she cuddled the shivering little girl inside the voluminous coat she wore. A group of neighbors surrounded Mimi, the rescue having interrupted the decorating of a huge wheelbarrow sitting in an open space between two houses.

When Arthur and Florence arrived, the three children were nudged inside. The glowing fire in the coal stove and hot soup provided comfort while questions were asked and answered.

Finally warmed and calmed, the three children walked outside to retrieve their sled for departure. The trip home now would be much longer. As they loaded Mimi into her seat, they stared with bewilderment at the red-ribboned wheelbarrow that was filled with a turkey and homemade bread and jarred green beans from someone's garden and a big white cauliflower hiding amid its green leaves, and a pie with the darkness of raisins bubbled through slits in its shiny pastry top.

"Our neighbor had a terrible accident some weeks ago," explained one of the men. "Timber in the mine where he works collapsed, and the cave-in left him with two broken legs. He'll be all right, but he won't be going to work for months."

"His family is having a hard time," a woman continued. "We were worried that they wouldn't have a Christmas dinner tomorrow, so we got all this food together. This evening we're going to wheel this load to their house and sing a few carols."

Arthur looked at Florence, Florence looked at Arthur, they both looked at 4-year-old Mimi huddled in a dry blanket someone had provided. She had been listening hard, making certain that she understood the story while she continued to clutch that can of corn. Meeting her brother's and sister's eyes, she asked a wordless question. Both nodded. She squirmed free of her blanket cocoon and walked purposefully to the decorated wheelbarrow where she dropped the can of corn inside. Florence dug into her jacket pocket, withdrew Mrs. Wheeler's little bag of sweet gifts, and placed it amid the food.

Carrying their rescuers' instructions and cautions in their heads, Arthur and Florence reestablished Mimi in her sled seat and began the long walk home, at a faster pace this time because they were eager to beat the dark and see their parents and sisters.

Around the dining table on Christmas Day, Charlie and Alice beamed with expressions of love and pride as they always did when they looked at their assembled children. They were growing up, and even little Mimi sat, for the first time, in a grown-up's chair for the festive holiday meal.

This Christmas was different in other ways too, for Alice and Charlie also were beaming with gratitude for Mimi's safe return from the terrifying river ride described to them on Christmas Eve. Along with enormous gratitude, they felt enormous pride, for now that Charlie and Alice knew the story of the Christmas wheelbarrow, they knew for certain that their children were good and generous people. Amid the turkey and stuffing and the cranberries and green beans followed by pies sweet with raisins and tart with apples from their own trees, no one at that Christmas table even noticed that corn kernels were few.

Christmas Flight

*F*lorence, Arthur, and Lucy agree that Nellie wore a red bow that long-ago Christmas morning. What they can't envision is how their parents, Charlie and Alice, could have tied a ribbon around that headstrong mare's scrawny neck since, apparently, she never wore anything after that gray, cold December day except, occasionally, a fearless kid on her back. For certain Nellie never tolerated a saddle or bridle, not even when old and only slightly more docile than she was that winter morning when she stomped and huffed her steamy breath while impatiently waiting to be presented as Santa's oversized surprise to three astonished kids.

Where Charlie and Alice got Nellie remains a mystery. All they told their children was that Nellie had come from the North Pole. Considering Nellie's antics, not even three naive kids in the first quarter of the twentieth century could have accepted that explanation because Nellie's fiery disposition had surely not been bred amid polar ice. Then too, had Santa harnessed her alongside Donner and Blitzen, his sleigh would have upset long before it reached Schuylkill County, Pennsylvania.

More likely the three children didn't care about Nellie's origin that holiday morning when they were bundled into coats, scarves, and hats that nearly covered their eyes to meet their galloping gift. These were the three family members who had wanted a horse, and she had arrived! If later they noticed she was a bony, mottled red-brown, somehow asymmetrical equine with a crazed look in her one sighted eye, they were oblivious to those observations on that Christmas morning. Instead, as the reality of Nellie's actually being theirs set in, they danced and squealed yelps of delight into the snow-heavy sky, nearly toppling their parents in an exuberant display of excitement, gratitude, and pure glee.

Not until late in the afternoon after the Christmas feast was eaten, the pie savored, and stocking treasures examined and compared did Arthur, Florence, and Lucy discover that Nellie was not exactly a cuddly pet or a sweet reward for good behavior. Rather, she was a supernatural force to respect and hold in awe. Approaching Nellie where she stood rocking her head back and forth in a fenced area previously devoted to unruly baseball games, the siblings chattered loudly. Standing where the sisters normally took turns tossing balls in the direction of the swinging bat of Arthur, who always insisted on being the perpetual designated hitter, they deliberated about where Nellie could take them and the order in which they would climb upon her back for a glorious first ride.

Since seniority was the undisputed rule in the family, Arthur strode right up to Nellie, jumped, and tried to throw one leg across her back. Nellie sidestepped the airborne boy, and he thudded onto home plate with a shocked grunt. After his repeated failed attempts before his giggling sisters, the brave Florence stepped up insisting she could be more successful. She wasn't, and with each failure the mortified Arthur was a little less embarrassed.

Finally, the frustrated trio decided to try a cooperative effort. Grabbing Lucy, the family's 7-year-old skinny daredevil, the other two lifted her and launched her in the general direction of Nellie. With arms and legs flailing, Lucy miraculously managed to connect with the frantic animal and actually right herself into a seated position while Nellie came as close to a gallop as possible in the confined place she would eventually recognize as home.

With their dubious victory achieved, Arthur and Florence were determined to join their sister on Nellie's slippery back. Climbing to the top of the fence, Arthur jumped toward a flying Nellie as she dashed past, and on the next circuit Florence did the same so that eventually all three were aboard. With the third breathless passenger's weight added to that of the other two, Nellie abruptly stopped, nearly unseating them.

Then, the story goes that Nellie thought about the situation. Even as adults the three are certain Nellie contemplated her options before she decided to give them a Christmas ride they would never forget. With acceleration worthy of a locomotive, Nellie jolted into a gallop so fast that she cleared the fence, catapulted over the nearby stream, and left house, sisters, parents, and makeshift barn behind. That horse ran so fast that when she got to the railroad tracks, she outraced a train and kept accelerating north until her speed lifted them aloft like a helium balloon.

"We flew," Arthur remembers, and Florence and Lucy nod their now-gray heads sharing his reminiscence. "All the way to Mahanoy City we went," the trio swears, "and when we got there, Nellie just put it in reverse and within minutes we had flown 30 miles south to Pine Grove. Backwards!" As they sped along, they watched with wonder as coal banks turned into barren fields swept clean of crops.

But Nellie was not only fast. She was smart, and as darkness began to descend, she turned her cargo toward home.

The return trip was magical. Each small community offered up its twinkling holiday lights to illuminate the darkness of the snowy sky with crystal snowflakes reflecting red and green while bells and carols from the county's churches and the dense, sweet aroma of pine quieted the exhilarated children with the wonder of the spectacle. Finally, as Nellie approached her new home, she gradually descended to earth so that, tired from her trip, she walked, just sedately walked, toward the house where Charlie and Alice were waiting for the children's return.

With eyes glittering and cheeks flushed, Arthur, Florence, and Lucy slid from Nellie's back at the door and hurried inside for a snack before bedtime. Not until later, with Mimi asleep and the rest of the children in their pajamas and slippers, did they put their heads together to whisper their guesses about what Nellie might have planned for New Year's Eve.

Winter Picnic

*A*s soon as my sister Reenie tugged downward on the kitchen window shade and, in that precise shade-lifting motion, let her hand travel upward, we immediately remembered a description from one of our pop's stories.

"The snow when I was little," he had told us many times, "was so deep that the only way out of the house was through the chimney." My brother, sisters, and I always looked at him skeptically. "Don't believe me?" he asked. "Just wait." He always nodded his head several times for emphasis when he guaranteed us, "It will happen again." Now, on this first morning of the new year, his prediction seemed to have come true.

With the window exposed, we gathered to look out at a world where none of the usual sights appeared familiar—not the leafless gage tree, not the gigantic rhododendrons in bud, not the arbor framework waiting for its grape vines. Only whiteness. Our gardens and everything around them looked as if they were wrapped in one gigantic cloud. Even the high coal bank I passed each day on my way to school took on the majesty of an alpine peak. Silence replaced our usual noisy banter, until, after a few minutes of spellbound gazing, all five of us raced off in different directions as though we had verbally agreed to check all 22 windows in the house including those narrow attic ones tucked under the eaves. Sure enough we agreed when we reassembled in the kitchen, the snow that had tumbled from the sky all night had piled up and up and up so high we wondered whether we could get out of the house.

"Let's go outside before Mom and Pop wake up," Art whispered as if trying not to wake them. "Maybe we'll have to climb out through the chimney," I suggested, feeling a surge of hope and excitement.

Suddenly we were in motion again, hauling our boots and jackets and ear-flapped caps from the cellarway where, along a shelf, the boots always lined up from Art's big ones to Mimi's tiny ones and the jackets hung above them from hooks that paraded downward, each above its very own step. Hastily bundled against the cold, we nearly tumbled over each other in our rush to the back door.

"I'll go first," Art stated firmly, asserting his first-born status and taking charge as he liked to do. When the door, which opened outward, didn't yield to his push, he leaned his shoulder against it and shoved as hard as he could. The door wouldn't budge. I leaned my weight against Art's back and pushed too, and eventually Lucy and Reenie pushed behind us. After what seemed like several minutes of straining, Art stepped back to rest and sent us sisters cascading backward one after the other like three cartoon characters. I couldn't help giggling, and Lucy and Reenie joined me. Art scowled with frustration. Mimi soberly studied our actions through the narrow slit between her hat and glasses.

Composing ourselves, we looked around the room for an alternate exit. Almost simultaneously all five pairs of eyes settled on a little latched door in the ceiling at the far end of our long kitchen. Pop had built it to seal the hole left by a chimney that once had served as a vent for a coal-burning heatrola that had occupied the spot where a cupboard for everyday dishes now stood. Art walked to the cupboard, turned his back to it, and, leaning against the shelf in the middle, lifted himself into a seated position before swiveling and rising to his knees. From that position, he reached up to turn the latch and pulled on the small door until it begrudgingly opened. Grunting and groaning, he pushed himself into the short chimney and scrambled onto the roof. When Art stepped outside, I could see sky and hear his exclamations of wonder.

"Florence, you're strong. You can give Mimi, Lucy, and Reenie big boosts," he called down to me. "When they're outside, I'll reach down and help you."

Reenie and I lifted Mimi toward the chimney. "Jump," we instructed her, and she seemed to fly into Art's waiting hands. The athletic Lucy refused help and somehow managed to reach the roof on her own. Lifting Reenie was left to me alone, but claiming she could do it herself, she climbed Art-style with hands and feet against the chimney sides as did I. At the chimney top we found that we could just step out onto the one flat area of our otherwise sharply pitched roof, now a field of snow beneath a stone-gray sky.

After our initial awe passed, we deliberated what to do. I remember Mimi lying on her back to make snow angels and Art playfully chasing Reenie and Lucy while I just made mental notes for the extraordinary story I would write once back inside. Of course we all threw snowballs. Then we built a snowman whose rotund body blended in so thoroughly with his platform that not until we picked fuzz from our hats to make his eyes and used a loose button from Art's jacket for his round mouth was he actually visible. His perfectly O-shaped mouth made him look so much as if he were singing that we joined our voices to his deep baritone in several choruses of *O Christmas Tree*. Just as we finished singing and stood back to admire our chubby friend, the clouds parted. Sun shone down so brightly that we danced and romped on a jeweled prairie until we heard our names called from the kitchen below.

"Uh oh," Mimi said, rolling her blue eyes. Huddling around the chimney, we looked down and saw our pop's equally blue eyes filled with excitement looking up. "Told you, didn't I?" he taunted.

"We want to have a picnic, Pop," I called down, seized suddenly with inspiration. Always I will remember his reply. "Okay. Mom and I will join you."

After what seemed like a long, long time, Pop stood on a chair to lift a large basket of food into Art's outstretched hands. We pulled our lightweight mama through that unused chimney now serving a purpose none of us could have imagined. With amazing agility Pop climbed up on his own and joined us for our picnic next to the sky.

Mom spread our picnic tablecloth, the one with the map of Cape Cod on it that we had bought on a glorious summer vacation, and we unpacked the basket of delicacies. We placed the jumbo thermos of hot chocolate on Truro, positioned the gooey, raisin-dotted cinnamon buns on Barnstable, and stacked seven sunrise-golden oranges near Provincetown, then sat around our bright table as if we were on a sandy beach. We watched silver smoke escape from distant neighbors' chimneys, spied the glint of one of the river's wandering tributaries, and listened to silence broken only by the sounds of finger-licking and lip-smacking sighs of contentment. I can't remember how we got back inside.

I guess maybe Mom and Pop took Mimi back down the chimney. I think Art, Reenie, Lucy, and I sat and slid down the snow drift that had blown against the back of our house. I'm sure we cleared a path to our door and shoveled a lot of snow on that day and for several days after. I'm also sure that late in the afternoon we ate our traditional New Year's meal—roast pork for luck, fluffy mashed potatoes, and boiled cabbage with melted butter. Spice cake with vanilla icing for dessert. Then we probably played games until bedtime, Pop and Art huddled over checkers and the rest of us around the Parcheesi board nearby. I guess we did those things because they were our annual traditions, but what I remember most clearly is that rooftop picnic. The seven of us around our Cape Cod tablecloth on its billowy white table so close to the sun is a still life for eternity.

Florence remembers . . .

The Gift

*D*rowning in the charcoal-colored waters of our river on that cold day in early January was the last thought in my mind when the thin ice I was testing crackled beneath my feet.

The long walk home at the end of the school day with my brother Art began as it always did with the passage between the narrow row houses of the tiny town and then out onto the road past trees and winter-barren fields until we reached a narrow path. There a steep hill climbed toward our house nestled in a valley on the other side. When we reached the path's entrance, Art stopped swinging his leather schoolbag and turned to me with those blue, sparkling eyes that so often invited me to join him for fun and excitement. "Before we go home, let's go see if the river's frozen," he suggested.

"It won't be." I continued to walk, this day carrying my schoolbag a bit more primly in keeping with my luxurious attire.

"Bet it is." Without hesitating, he turned in the direction of the river road. "Come on."

"Not today." I stood still with temptation swirling around me. "I might get my coat dirty."

Foremost in my reluctance was the fear of soiling my new coat—my beautiful, white, fur-soft coat that my mom had given me for Christmas. Allowing me to wear it to school on the first day after the holiday vacation was as impractical as buying a white coat for a 10-year-old girl with tomboy tendencies. Still I had begged, and Mom had indulged my desire to have my classmates and Miss Larrison, my teacher, appreciate my newly found glamour. Entering the schoolyard that morning was glorious. Miss Larrison smiled at me and told me how pretty I looked when I passed by her as she stood in the doorway of our two-room schoolhouse greeting each of her pupils as if he or she had been away for many years. One of Art's classmates, a cute, sixth-grade boy, whistled through his teeth. My girlfriends circled me in admiration. I was, on that one thrilling morning, the focus of attention, maybe even of envy, and I savored the unfamiliar taste.

"You won't even be near the water," Art insisted. "We'll be careful. We'll just take one quick look and then go home."

As it always did, the ever-changing Schuylkill River, dirty though it was, called to me while my persuasive brother, who held so much influence over me, soothed my worries. Without being aware of making a decision, I watched him until just before he disappeared around the road's first bend and then ran after him the way I always did.

When we reached the river bank, Art started down, his heavy brown boots sliding in the mud and slush of melted snow. Lifting my coat, I clambered after him, my rubber overshoes sticking a little with each step. Then the sheen of glimmering ice appeared—the river with its murky water garbed in a glaze of light.

"Told you," Art bragged as he began to tightrope walk along the icy edge. Whatever had made me reluctant to risk the purity of my precious Christmas gift was exchanged for the lure of ice walking, and while my big brother navigated the river's edge, I ventured out onto a fascinating, fragile stage befitting my starlet's attire. For a magical moment the bewitching glimmer alone held me secure.

I heard rather than saw the shattering and was jolted into reality by the sting of icy water rising over my overshoes, up my legs, over my body. "Help!" I heard myself shrieking.

Art turned toward my voice. Terror in his eyes, he ran, slipping through the ice into the water's shallow edge as he scrambled toward me. "I'll save you," he shouted as I struggled to get my footing. I grabbed his outstretched hand. Already I was crying, not because I was hurt or cold or frightened though I was the latter two, but because my new, my beautiful fur-soft coat was soggy and smeared with streaks of our river's coal-infused water.

All the way home I cried while running toward what I most feared, my mother's expression of horror and anticipated rage. I sobbed and stumbled and wailed, "Mom's going to be so mad at me." Images of my mom's proud expression when she gave me the coat, purchased with scarce money earned through her hard work, flooded my mind. Disappointing her was more punishing than fearing possible punishments I might receive, more painful than a ruined gift that had made me feel beautiful.

"It was an accident," Art feebly repeated as he kept pace beside me. Intermittently he asked, "Why did you do it?" revealing his worried suspicion that he would be blamed for the reckless escapade.

Only when I reached the back door of our house did I slow enough to take a deep breath before bursting into the warm kitchen. Glints of fire flickered in the coal stove, and mixed smells of raw onion and freshly baked bread cooling on a cabinet shelf filled the room. Mom was bending over the table rolling dough with her heavy, red-handled rolling pin while a brimming pan of sliced potatoes, onions, and chunks of beef awaited its pastry crown. She turned when the door slammed, then rushed toward me as soon as she saw my disheveled appearance and flushed, tear-smeared face.

"What happened?" she asked, hurriedly wiping flour from her hands onto her apron. "Where are you hurt?"

"I'm not hurt," I sobbed, tears streaming again.

"Then why are you crying?" she asked more quietly.

"My coat, my beautiful coat is ruined," I answered, gasping for breath.

"Oh, don't cry about that," she told me, helping me to undress. "I can wash it. It will be so clean that you'll never know anything happened."

Seating me on one of our straight-backed, wooden kitchen chairs, she leaned over to remove my muddy overshoes, all the while murmuring reassurances. Surrounded by the familiar warmth and aromas of our kitchen, I laid my throbbing head on her shoulder, sighed, and rested as she placed her hand, heavy with comfort, on my damp curls.

On that afternoon, with her assurances, I never doubted that my mother could clean my coat and make it look like new. She did, but what I remember most is that she wasn't angry. I can still feel my head on her shoulder, her hand on my head. Years later she would lay her head on my shoulder while I smoothed her wispy white hair. Now, even more years later, for comfort I rest against my daughter's shoulder and feel on my head the surprising weight of her light hand.

With admiration and gratitude ...

for my late Aunt Elsie, who, in writing our family's genealogy, demonstrated the virtue of painstaking research, a devotion to historical accuracy, and the flair of a gifted novelist.

Sherrill Silberling and JoAnne Doyle were longtime colleagues in the Pottsville Area School District in Pottsville, PA. This is their first collaboration.

About the author...

Sherrill has had a passion for words since she first learned to put them on paper. In her career as a teacher on both high school and college levels, she taught her students to communicate through words written and spoken and to appreciate the words of the world's great writers. Writing has always been her avocation. Her work has been published in regional, state, and national periodicals including the *Harrisburg Patriot* and *Pottsville Republican* newspapers, *Schuylkill Living Magazine*, *Wild Onions*, the fine arts journal of Penn State's Milton S. Hershey Medical Center, and *English Journal*. Her poetry has received recognition in regional competitions.

About the artist...

With undergraduate and graduate degrees in art education, JoAnne enjoyed teaching art to middle school students throughout her career. She continues to teach adult classes and private students and has served as a volunteer artist for the local Make-A-Wish chapter for 17 years. As a professional artist she has painted murals and does calligraphy and illustrations. Primarily a pen and ink specialist, she has been commissioned by numerous organizations and businesses to create architectural drawings. Her works are displayed publicly throughout the region.

Made in the USA
Middletown, DE
07 March 2021

34978761R00031